# FIND
## THE REAL
# MOTHER
# GOOSE

## Note to Parents

The Real Mother Goose has long been a favorite of children. Now they can read her rhymes, see her delightful characters, and search for hidden pictures. In each full-color illustration, children will find a rhyme as well as an instruction to search for objects relating to the rhyme. Some of these objects are in plain view, while others, including The Real Mother Goose herself, are hidden.

# FIND
## THE REAL
# MOTHER
# GOOSE.

Illustrated by
Patty McCloskey

# CHECKERBOARD PRESS
NEW YORK

# LITTLE BO-PEEP

Little Bo-Peep has lost her sheep,
And can't tell where to find
them;
Leave them alone, and they'll come
home,
And bring their tails behind
them.

❦❦

Little Bo-Peep has not only lost her 18
sheep, but she is also missing 8 cows,
5 pigs, and the Real Mother Goose!
Can you help her find them?

# HANDY PANDY

Handy Pandy, Jack-a-dandy,
Loves plum cake and sugar candy.
He bought some at a grocer's shop,
And out he came, hop, hop, hop!

Can you help Handy Pandy find his
favorite candy in this picture? Look very
carefully and you will see 4 lollipops,
6 peppermint sticks, 7 pieces of wrapped
candy, and the Real Mother Goose!

GROCER
SHOP

## SIMPLE SIMON

Simple Simon met a pieman,
  Going to the fair;
Says Simple Simon to the pieman,
  "Let me taste your ware."

While Simple Simon is on his way to
the fair, help him find 7 pies, 5 pails,
8 birds, and the Real Mother Goose!

# MISS MUFFET

Little Miss Muffet
Sat on a tuffet,
Eating of curds and whey;
There came a big spider,
And sat down beside her,
And frightened Miss Muffet away.

Although one spider frightened Miss Muffet, there are 15 more in her room. Can you find them? There are also 4 bowls, 4 spoons, and the Real Mother Goose to find!

WEST 1mi

EAST 1mi

# THE CROOKED SIXPENCE

There was a crooked man, and he
went a crooked mile,
He found a crooked sixpence beside a crooked stile;
He bought a crooked cat, which
caught a crooked mouse,
And they all lived together in a
little crooked house.

The crooked man found a crooked
sixpence, but he has lost 6 cats, 6 rats,
5 crooked hats, and the Real Mother
Goose! Can you help him find them?

# BANBURY CROSS

Ride a cock-horse to Banbury Cross,
To see an old lady upon a white horse.
Rings on her fingers, and bells on
    her toes,
She shall have music wherever she goes.

This fine lady has rings on her fingers and
bells on her toes, but elsewhere on this
page are 2 more rings, as well as 4 horns,
3 drums, 7 bells, 2 fiddles, 2 lutes, and the
Real Mother Goose. Can you find them?

## HUMPTY DUMPTY

Humpty Dumpty sat on a wall,
Humpty Dumpty had a great fall;
All the King's horses, and all the
    King's men
Cannot put Humpty Dumpty together
    again.

❀❀

The King's men are too late to keep
Humpty Dumpty from falling off the wall,
but you can take your time to find 6 bugles,
6 drums, 6 crowns, and the Real Mother
Goose!

## OLD KING COLE

Old King Cole
Was a merry old soul,
And a merry old soul was he;
He called for his pipe,
And he called for his bowl,
And he called for his fiddlers three!

Old King Cole needs your help to find his 4 pipes, 4 bowls, 6 fiddles, 4 crowns, and the Real Mother Goose!

## THE CAT AND THE FIDDLE

Hey, diddle, diddle!
The cat and the fiddle,
The cow jumped over the moon;
The little dog laughed
To see such sport,
And the dish ran away with the spoon.

Hey, diddle, diddle! Can you find 3 cats,
3 dogs, 3 cows, 3 fiddles, 3 dishes, 3 spoons,
and the Real Mother Goose?

# OLD MOTHER HUBBARD

Old Mother Hubbard
Went to the cupboard,
  To give her poor dog a bone;
But when she got there
The cupboard was bare,
  And so the poor dog had none.

❀

Old Mother Hubbard's cupboard may be
bare, but her cottage contains 3 bones,
8 hats, 6 cats, 5 rats, and the Real
Mother Goose!

# SING A SONG OF SIXPENCE

Sing a song of sixpence,
 A pocket full of rye;
Four-and-twenty blackbirds
 Baked in a pie!

Four and twenty birds may
have been baked in a pie,
but 16 of them have flown out
and are hiding! Can you find
them, as well as 8 hidden pies,
1 little mouse, and the Real
Mother Goose?

# THE HOUSE THAT JACK BUILT

This is the house that Jack built.
This is the malt
That lay in the house that Jack built.

This is the rat,
That ate the malt
That lay in the house that Jack built.

There are 4 rats, 4 cats, 4 dogs, 4
cows, 4 milk buckets, and the Real
Mother Goose around the house that
Jack built. Can you find them all?